KS4 Citizenship

The Workbook

No, it's not another boring workbook — this one lets you
have a good rant about things that actually matter to you.

As well as testing you know the facts, each page has discussion
questions to really get you thinking and forming your own opinions.

The book covers everything you need to learn for KS4 Citizenship
and is ideal for use with our KS4 Citizenship Study Guide.

Contents

Contents

Published by Coordination Group Publications

Contributors:

Elizabeth Butcher   Alan Rix
Martin Chester   Ed Robinson
Taissa Csaky   Emma Singleton
Dominic Hall   Peter Townsend
Simon Little   Lynda Turner
Becky May   Jennifer Underwood
Kate Redmond   Julie Wakeling

ISBN: 1-84146-964-5

Groovy website: www.cgpbooks.co.uk

With thanks to Suzie Almond for the proofreading.
Jolly bits of clipart from CorelDRAW

Printed by Elanders Hindson, Newcastle upon Tyne

Citizenship

Q1 Look these words up in a dictionary, and write down the definitions. If a word has lots of definitions write down the ones that you think are most relevant to studying citizenship.

a) citizen

b) state

c) government

d) community

e) right

f) responsibility

Citizens of the Universe, join with me or perish!

Q2 Different people have different ideas about what it means to be a citizen. What do you think 'citizen' means in each of the sentences below? Match each sentence to one of the definitions of 'citizen' given in the box.

a) *Mrs. Jeffries from down the road is a model citizen: she does meals on wheels for housebound people and always picks up after her dog.*

b) In ancient Athens, all adult men who were not slaves were classed as citizens and could vote in the General Assembly.

c) **PASSPORT CONTROL: UK citizens this way** ▷

Someone who can take part in the political system.

Somebody who plays a part in a community.

Someone who can prove that they belong to a particular country.

DISCUSSION QUESTION Q3 In the UK, when you turn 18 you get the right to vote in local and national elections.

Why is it important to use your vote? Give as many reasons you can.

*Try to keep your answer quite general here — think about things that might be used to help persuade **everyone** to vote.*

DISCUSSION QUESTION Q4 In your own words explain what is meant by 'citizenship'.

Citizen Kane — a great citizen, according to film buffs...

'Citizen Kane' is an American film about a man who sets up a newspaper empire. It was made in 1941 and stars Orson Welles. Critics would always put it top of 100 Greatest Films Ever Made polls. But then along came 'Love Actually' and everything changed. Anyway, on with the citizenship...

Human Rights

Q1   Copy out this table about human rights from history and finish it off.

Document	Written when?	Written where?	Rights described?
Magna Carta			Right to fair trial before imprisonment for landowners.
American Declaration of Independence	1776		
Declaration of the Rights of Man		Paris, France	

Q2   Match up the beginnings of the phrases below to their correct endings. Each phrase describes a human right that you're entitled to according to the *Declaration of Human Rights*.

a)   the right to a free   i)   opinion and expression

b)   freedom from   ii)   proven guilty

c)   freedom of   iii) slavery

d)   innocent until   iv)   education

Q3   From the list below copy out the sentences which describe abuses of human rights.

a)   Being put in prison for speaking out against your country's government.

b)   Being put into prison for committing murder.

c)   Not getting a job because you're female.

d)   Having to pay university fees.

e)   Being arrested when you're caught breaking into a car.

f)   Being put into prison without having a fair trial in court.

DISCUSSION QUESTION Q4   According to the *Universal Declaration of Human Rights* we are all entitled to the same human rights.

Find a news story that covers violation of human rights. Say which rights are being violated and who is committing the violation. Describe what is being done to protect the human rights or make suggestions about what could be done.

DISCUSSION QUESTION Q5   In some places (e.g. certain states in the USA) the death penalty is still used for people who are convicted of murder.

Do you think this is OK, or do you think it represents a violation of human rights? Write down the main points from your discussion.

Human Rights

Q1   Copy and complete this paragraph using words from the box.

48 .... from the .... have signed

the *Universal Declaration of Human Rights*. The Declaration is made up

of .... When one of these is broken, it's known as

a ....

United Nations
violation
member states
articles

Q2   When written, the *Universal Declaration of Human Rights* was meant to apply to every person in the world. But in reality, the articles can be hard to enforce.

a)   Look at the articles below and explain why each one might be hard to enforce.

Article 4   Everyone has the right to freedom from slavery.

Article 19   Everyone has the right to freedom of opinion and expression.

Article 23   Everyone has the right to work.

b)   Copy and complete the table below. The first column lists articles from the declaration and the second gives examples of how each article could be violated.

ARTICLE	E.G. OF VIOLATION
Everyone is entitled to all the rights in the Declaration.	i)
ii)	Not allowed to print a story in a newspaper.
Everyone is innocent until proven guilty.	iii)
Everyone has the right to a free education.	iv)
v)	Refused a job because of a disability.

 Q3   Calling it the **Universal** Declaration of Human Rights is a bit misleading because many countries don't agree with, or stick to, all the articles.

Think of some real-life examples of countries not following articles
in the declaration and discuss why they might choose not to.
Then write an imaginary letter from a leader of one of the countries,
explaining your reasons for not following the Declaration.

 Q4   Read the full Declaration at www.un.org/Overview/rights.
If you can't get on the net there should be a copy in your school or local library.

Rewrite the list putting all the articles in order of importance — start with
the one that's most important to you and end with the least important.
Discuss your reasons for putting the rights into this order.

Universal-ish might be a more honest description...
Some people think the *Universal Declaration of Human Rights* is never going to be all that universal.
After all only 48 countries have signed it and there are 200-odd in the world...

__Human Rights Law__

Q1   Match up each thing from the box below with the correct definition of what it does.

> European Court of Human Rights   European Commission of Human Rights
>
> European Convention of Human Rights

a) It contains articles about human rights that are based on the Universal Declaration of Human Rights.

b) Countries that violate articles of the Convention are tried here.

c) It checks that human rights are being upheld in keeping with the European Convention of Human Rights.

Q2   Copy and complete these sentences about the European Commission on Human Rights.

a) The Commission is made up of .... judges.

b) Each judge comes from a different member country of the ....

c) Judges are elected every .... years.

Q3   The Human Rights Act became law in the UK in 2000.
     Choose the best word from each pair to finish off the sentences.

a) The Human Rights Act is a **British/European** law.

b) British judges and courts can **interpret/overrule** the European Convention on Human Rights.

c) The Human Rights Act allows for individual rights to be restricted when they threaten the rights of the **Government/community** as a whole.

DISCUSSION
QUESTION   Q4   In each of these situations, you could say the person has been denied a human right.
                 For each one (i) decide which right it is
                              (ii) suggest why it is being denied.

- Ken wants to release a video of a really gory fight he was in at the local boxing club. The censor won't allow it.

- A former member of the SAS is banned from publishing a book about his part in a recent anti-terrorist mission.

- A man who is seriously mentally ill and convicted of assault is kept in a hospital prison for life. The usual punishment for assault is just a few years.

- Sarah is held at a police station overnight. The police haven't charged her.

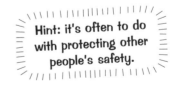

Hint: it's often to do with protecting other people's safety.

Your Legal Rights at Home and School

Q1   Copy out the paragraph below, choosing the correct word each time you have a choice.

> Your parents or guardians are responsible for feeding, clothing and *(cleaning/housing)* you. You should be protected from *(violence/swearing)*, abuse and *(neglect/disease)*. Your rights are *(protected/prevented)* in the UN Declaration of Human *(Rights/Race)*.

Q2   What rights do you have at school?
Write a paragraph using ALL of the words in the box below.

> safety   education   emotional
>
> abuse   race   sex
>
> physical   discrimination

 Q3   We all have responsibilities to others — whether it means respecting another's rights or looking after a little brother or sister. What responsibilities do you have to:

a) your family?

b) your friends?

c) your local community?

Try to come up with at least three
ideas for a), b) and c).

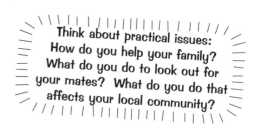
Think about practical issues:
How do you help your family?
What do you do to look out for
your mates? What do you do that
affects your local community?

Q4   Sarah is being bullied in school. She needs to talk to someone about what is happening. A friend gives her three options — talk to her parents, talk to her teachers or contact Childline.

What are the advantages and disadvantages of each
group of people Sarah could confide in?

You should be protected from violence, neglect and Westlife...

All this human rights malarkey is like a blue whale on a tightrope — a huge balancing act.
Individual rights have to be balanced against the rights of other people in the community.

Your Legal Rights at Work

Q1 Complete the following sentences by choosing the correct endings.

a) In most jobs…

b) If you undertake voluntary work…

c) If you opt for full-time work…

i) … you normally work 5 days a week.

ii) … you are paid for the work you do.

iii) …you give your time and skills free of charge.

Q2 Choose the three most appropriate phrases from the list below to describe your rights at work.

I'm not wearing that horror for any money.

Comfortable shoes	Equal pay for equal work	Smoking breaks
Free meals	Safety from injury	Soft loo roll
Fashionable uniforms	Higher wages for women	Sick pay and paid holiday

DISCUSSION QUESTION Q3 Young people are allowed to work, under strict guidelines, from the age of 14. Copy out this table and do a survey to find out what work people in your class do and why.

Name	Job	Hours/week	Reason for working

Most young people who work do newspaper rounds or babysitting.

DISCUSSION QUESTION Q4 After the general election in 1997, the Labour government introduced a minimum wage for workers aged 18 and over. There is no minimum wage for workers aged between 16 and 18 and in full-time employment.

Do you think the government should introduce a minimum wage for young people?

You could argue that younger people have less experience so deserve less pay. Or you could say everyone should be assessed individually.

Consumer Rights

Q1 Consumer law protects your rights as a consumer.

a) Which two of these laws deal with consumer rights?

Sale of Goods Act   *Highways Act*   *Trades Description Act*

b) For each of your choices in a) give a brief description of what the law does.

Use what you've learnt in class or what you can find out on the internet to help you with this.

Q2 For each of the phrases below write a sentence about your consumer rights.

fair price   reasonable quality   advertising   safe product

Q3 These statements are all about your power and rights as a consumer. Write down whether each one is true or false. Rewrite the false ones to make them true.

a) Local Authority Trading Standards Officers enforce consumer law.

b) If you live in the UK you are protected by UK consumer law for everything you buy — even when it's from abroad.

c) When you buy goods from UK stores over the internet you're covered by the same laws that protect you when you buy in a shop.

DISCUSSION QUESTION Q4 Discuss what rights you would have as a consumer in each of the following situations and what you would do:

a) You buy a new T-shirt in a sale but when you get home you find it's ripped.

b) You buy a CD from a high street music store. It is sealed but when you open the packet at home the CD is scratched.

c) You take a film of holiday photos to be processed on a 1 hour service. When you return the assistant tells you your pictures will not be ready until the next day.

d) You buy a bicycle from an advert in your local paper which turns out to have been stolen.

DISCUSSION QUESTION Q5 Consumers are a powerful group who can make big changes. Fifteen years ago it was very hard to find organic or 'fair trade' foods. Now they are in most supermarkets.

What role do you think consumers have played in making these foods more widely available?

Fair trade food is bought direct from farmers in developing countries allowing them to make a bigger (fairer) profit.

Waiter, waiter, there's a fly in my soup...

"I'm so terribly sorry madam. Let me replace your soup with a fresh fly-free bowl free of charge and offer the unreserved apologies of the kitchen, the management and all the waiting staff."

Animal Rights

Q1   Give an example of how humans use animals for each of the following:

   a)   transport
   b)   protection
   c)   medical research
   d)   detecting criminals

   e)   food
   f)   clothes
   g)   companionship
   h)   entertainment

Q2   For each of these statements say whether it is true or false in the UK. Rewrite the false statements to make them true.

   a)   Bull-fighting is legal.

   b)   There is no minimum standard for the care of pigs in pork farming.

   c)   Whale hunting is illegal.

   d)   Battery hen farms have to stick to guidelines on minimum living standards.

   e)   Every dog owner has to have a dog-owners license to prove they can care for their dog.

If you don't know the answers, do some research and find out.

Q3   Pro fox-hunting campaigners say that over half the British public supports hunting.

   a)   Write down two arguments for fox-hunting and two against.

   b)   Explain your own opinion about fox-hunting.

DISCUSSION QUESTION Q4   Read the extract below then answer the questions.

Cambridge-based Huntingdon Life Sciences, has once again been targeted by campaigners against animal testing. Yesterday a letter bomb addressed to a senior research scientist was intercepted and deactivated. In recent months many employees have received 'hate mail' but this is the first letter bomb for some time...

Do you think it's acceptable for campaigners to use violence?
How else could campaigners get their views across?

DISCUSSION QUESTION Q5   Humans often use animals for entertainment. Is this right or wrong?

Write a mini-essay. Start by describing arguments for and against using animals in entertainment, then write a conclusion explaining your opinion.

Remember — a dog's not just for Xmas — save some for Boxing Day

Fox-hunting causes some really heated discussions. If you go to a school in the country where some people hunt, try not to rip each other's hair out. Everyone's got a right to be heard...

Identity

Q1 Answer these questions about your identity.

a) Copy out this diagram and label each circle so it describes you.

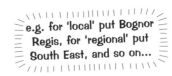
e.g. for 'local' put Bognor Regis, for 'regional' put South East, and so on...

Q2 Say whether each of these identities is an **ethnic identity** or a **religious identity**.

a) Catholic   c) Sikh   e) Punjabi   g) Amish

b) Afro-Caribbean   d) Irish   f) Jewish   h) Puerto Rican

Q3 When England won the Rugby World Cup in 2003 many English people felt much more patriotic than usual.

Make a list of any other events you can think of that have made you or other people feel more patriotic and discuss why you think the events had this effect.

Q4 Some people hang the Union Jack outside their businesses. Others wear it on clothes. Other people don't like it and don't want to be seen as "flag-wavers".

Write a mini-essay describing your feelings about the Union Jack and where and how you think it should be used.

Q5 Read these statements about being British.

"My Grandad's a true Brit. He was on the submarines in the Second World War, and he played cricket for Sussex for twenty years."

"I was born in Nigeria and moved here when I was 10. I've still got lots of family in Nigeria, but I got married and had my kids here so I'm definitely British now."

Do you think either statement is a better definition of being British?

Feminists want it renamed the Union Jill...

I never feel all that British till I go abroad. Then the further I get from crumpets and cups of tea, the more British I feel. Just imagine — there are whole countries out there with no crumpets.

Multiculturalism in Britain

Q1 Write down the statement that best describes a "multicultural society".

- You can get food and hear music from all around the world.

- People are mostly from the same ethnic group.

- People are from lots of different ethnic groups.

- Nobody minds if people come and settle from other countries.

Q2 Copy out the paragraph below and use the words from the box to fill in the gaps.

> cultures   ethnic   diversity   respect
>
> interesting   multicultural   citizens

Britain is a .... society. People from many different ....
backgrounds live and work here. Cultural .... in Britain has brought many
benefits and makes it a more .... place to live. It's important for
.... of a multicultural society to .... cultural differences.

Q3 The leader of an extreme political group has written to the local paper calling
for all businesses owned by people from ethnic minorities to be closed down.

Write a reply to the letter.

Explain why the community would be better off with the businesses than without them.

 Q4 At the 2001 census, approximately 7.9% of the 55 million people living
in the UK described themselves as belonging to an ethnic minority.

How does living in a multicultural society affect your daily life?
In a group, make a list as long as you can of ways that cultural
diversity influences popular culture in the UK.

 Q5 Read this statement.

> The 1996 British Crime Survey estimated that 382,000 offences (just over 2%
> of all offences) were considered by the victim to be motivated by racism.

a) Do you think this statistic covers all cases of racism in 1996?

b) In general what problems do you think there could be
with getting an accurate picture of racism in Britain?

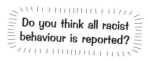
Do you think all racist behaviour is reported?

Racial Issues in Britain

Q1   The British population has always had a mix of ethnic groups. Write down all the ethnic groups from the box that have settled here in the past.

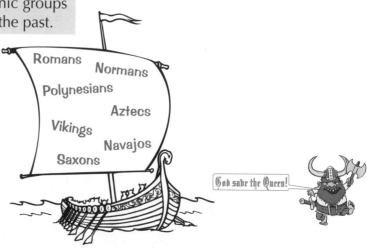

Romans Normans
Polynesians
           Aztecs
Vikings
        Navajos
Saxons

God save the Queen!

Q2   Copy out this paragraph, choosing the better word from each pair.

Lots of (*racists / immigrants*) have settled in Britain over the years. Many were encouraged to come and (*work / trade*) here following the end of (*World War I / World War II*). More recently, many asylum seekers and refugees have come here to (*escape / prevent*) problems in their own country such as war. Other people come here in search of better opportunities for work and (*education / entertainment*).

Q3   Some of these could be examples of racial discrimination. Say which ones could be and which definitely aren't. Explain your choices.

a)   The police stop and search a young black man in the street.

b)   An Asian woman is sentenced to life imprisonment for committing murder.

c)   An African-Caribbean man earns less than a white man for doing the same job.

d)   An Asian man fails his driving test three times in a row.

e)   A white boy and Chinese boy are caught dealing drugs at school.
       Only the Chinese boy is excluded from school.

DISCUSSION QUESTION Q4   Research by the Commission for Racial Equality shows that in the UK people from ethnic minorities are more likely to be unemployed than white people.

Do you think this shows evidence of racial discrimination?
Talk about it as a group then write up the conclusions of your discussion.

DISCUSSION QUESTION Q5   A large proportion of those convicted for racist offences are under 17 years old.

Write down some ideas for dealing with racist attitudes in young people.

Racial Issues in Britain

Q1   This question's about some of the ways people have suggested we can deal with racism.
Copy out the table and fill it in by choosing words and phrases from the box to fill the blanks.

CAUSE OF RACIAL TENSION	POSSIBLE SOLUTION
Ignorance of other cultures	
	Integration

Promote equality

Racial discrimination

Education

Segregated communities

Q2   You have to look carefully at statistics to be sure of what they prove.

a)   Which of these statistics would be most helpful if you were looking for
evidence of racial discrimination in the employment of teachers?

- The number of ethnic minority teachers in employment
  compared to the number of white teachers in employment.

Remember that about 8%
of people in the UK are
from ethnic minorities.

- The percentage of white applicants who are offered teaching jobs compared to
  the percentage of ethnic minority applicants who are offered teaching jobs.

- The number of people from ethnic minorities who apply for teaching jobs
  compared to the number of white people who apply for teaching jobs.

b)   Explain your choice for a).

DISCUSSION QUESTION Q3   In 1993 a black teenager, Stephen Lawrence, was murdered by a group of
young white males. The case highlighted many problems in British society.

Read up on the Stephen Lawrence case in books and on the internet, and make
some notes on it. What do you think the case reveals about racism in Britain?
Discuss your findings.

DISCUSSION QUESTION Q4   Riots in Oldham and Bradford hit the headlines in 2001. The riots in both
towns involved violence between white and ethnic minority communities.

How can local authorities try and prevent similar riots happening again?
Draw up an action plan for ways to improve race relations within a community.

Racism is a dangerous force...

It's bad enough to be on the receiving end of racist namecalling. Racism gets even more serious
when it affects people's chance of getting a job or just living a normal decent life.

Conflict in the Community

Q1   Copy and complete the sentences below, using words from the box to fill in the blanks. You can use words more than once.

| extreme | Loyalists | paramilitary | Protestant | Ireland | Nationalists | Catholic | the UK | violence |

a)   Unionists and .... mainly have .... members.
They want to see the continued union of Northern Ireland and ....

b)   .... and Republicans mainly have .... members.
They want to see Northern Ireland united with the rest of ....

c)   Republicans and .... are the more .... political parties on each side.
Followers include .... groups that use .... to get their message across.

Q2   Match up each of the Northern Irish political parties, a)-e), with the best description.

a) UUP   i)   *Loyalist paramilitary group*
b) Sinn Féin   ii) *Unionist party*
c) SDLP   iii) *Republican paramilitary group*
d) UDA   iv) *Legal political party of the Republicans*
e) IRA   v)   *Nationalist party*

Q3   Describe 3 positive steps in the peace process in Northern Ireland and 3 setbacks that have slowed the peace process down.

 Q4   The number of IRA volunteers rose dramatically after Bloody Sunday (30 January 1972) when British soldiers fired on a civil rights march in Northern Ireland.

a)   Make a list of reasons why people might have volunteered for the IRA after Bloody Sunday.

Use your library or the internet to find out more about Northern Ireland and Bloody Sunday.

b)   Write down all the ways you can think of that Bloody Sunday might have complicated the conflict in Northern Ireland even further.

 Q5   British soldiers are still present in Northern Ireland. Their job is to try and prevent violent conflict. Unionists and Loyalists generally support their presence but Nationalists and Republicans see them as an 'occupying force'.

Do you think there should be a British army presence in Northern Ireland? Make two lists — one showing how British soldiers in Northern Ireland could help the peace process and one showing how they could slow it down.

It'll all be sorted out — eventually...

The conflict in Northern Ireland's been going on for decades now. Things have improved loads recently but there's still a fair bit of work to be done before the whole thing's sorted for good.

UK Relations with Europe

Q1   Which of these countries are **not** members of the European Union?

    Ukraine   Germany   Italy   Spain   France   Norway   United Kingdom

Q2   These questions are about the government of the European Union.

    a)   Write down the correct description for each group.

European Parliament	Council of Ministers	European Commission

writes new economic, environmental, social and foreign policy   *makes the final decision on policies drawn up by the Commission*   *debates policies suggested by Commission and suggests amendments*

    b)   Explain how the members of each group above are chosen.

    c)   Do you think the government of the European Union is fully democratic? Write a mini-essay to explain your answer.

Q3   Which of the following rights did you gain in 1997 when you became a European citizen?

    a) The right to move permanently to any EU country.

    b) The right to freedom of opinion and expression.

    c) The right to health care and social benefits anywhere in the European Union.

    d) The right to work or study in any EU country.

    e) The right to a fair trial.

Q4   When the Euro became official currency in most of Europe in 2002 the UK did not join.

    Write a list of advantages and a list of disadvantages to Britain of joining the Euro.

Q5   Read this extract from a report on the 1999 European elections, then look at the questions below.

> In the European elections held in 1999, 24% of the UK's electorate voted. This was a low turnout compared to other countries, for example Germany, where 45.2% of the electorate voted, and Italy, where 70% of the electorate voted.

In a group come up with as many arguments as you can to persuade people to vote at the next European election.

UK Relations with the Rest of the World

Q1   Write out all these organisations in the order they were formed.

NATO   League of Nations   Warsaw Pact   United Nations

Q2   Copy and complete the following sentences about the UN. Use words from the box to fill the gaps.

global   peaceful   prevent   United Nations

economic sanctions   peacekeeping   cooperation

The UK is one of 191 members of the .... The UN aims to

encourage ...., help find ....

solutions to disputes and .... human rights violations.

The UN has the power to impose .... on a country and then

send in .... troops if they continue to ignore UN resolutions.

Q3   Answer these questions about NATO.

a)   What do the letters NATO stand for?

b)   NATO is a 'defensive alliance'. Explain what this means.

c)   What was NATO's first military action?

d)   In 1991 the Warsaw Pact broke up. Explain how this changed NATO's purpose.

NUTO — the armed rodent defence force with nerves of steel

DISCUSSION QUESTION Q4   NATO and the United Nations were both formed soon after the Second World War.

Make a list of differences and similarities between NATO and the UN.

Think about which countries belong to the two organisations and what the purpose of each organisation is.

DISCUSSION QUESTION Q5   In 2003 the UK and the USA went to war in Iraq without the backing of the UN.

Make a list of ways the UN can help the UK and ways the USA can help the UK. Do you think it's more important for the UK to have good relations with the USA or the UN?

Waterloo and Gare du Nord — the united stations...

UN, NATO, League of Nations, Warsaw Pact — it can all get pretty confusing. But it's important stuff if you want to understand world politics, and Britain's relationship with the rest of the world.

The Commonwealth

Q1 These sentences about the Commonwealth are all slightly wrong. Rewrite them so they give correct statements.

a) The British Commonwealth of Nations was formed in 1918.

b) Most British colonies won their independence in the years following the First World War.

c) Ex-colonies had no choice about whether or not they would join the Commonwealth.

d) The Archbishop of Canterbury is the official head of the Commonwealth.

e) Mexico is the only country in the Commonwealth which is not a former British colony.

Q2 Write out this paragraph, filling in the gaps with words from the box.

In the early days of the Commonwealth, Britain had .... with other members and agreements to give other members .... if they were attacked. Britain now has trade agreements with the .... which have become more important than those with former colonies and most Commonwealth countries now have strong enough .... to be able to defend themselves.

| military aid | armies | European Union | trade agreements |

Q3 Explain what each of these does in the Commonwealth.

a) Commonwealth Heads of State

b) Secretariat

c) Commonwealth Ministerial Action Group

DISCUSSION QUESTION Q4 "The Commonwealth is an outdated concept which serves no useful purpose."

Do you agree?

How important are the meetings of Commonwealth Heads of State? What about the Commonwealth Games?

DISCUSSION QUESTION Q5 Read this extract from an article on the 'banana wars' of the 1990s.

In the 1975 Lome Agreement, EU countries agreed to buy as many bananas as Caribbean countries could produce. The US government saw this as a threat to 'free trade' and appealed to the World Trade Organisation. In 1997 the WTO agreed with the US that the Lome Agreement was unfair and the EU had to drop it.

In a group discuss why European countries made agreements like the Lome Agreement in the first place, and why the WTO said it was unfair.

British Issues Abroad

Q1   Explain each of the terms below.

    a)   disaster relief

    b)   World Bank

    c)   bilateral aid

    d)   peacekeeping troops

Q2   Following the terrorist attacks on the USA on 11 September 2001, the USA declared a 'war on terrorism'.

    a)   Why were NATO countries expected to get involved in the 'war on terrorism'?

    b)   Why did the US and Britain go to war in Afghanistan following the 11 September attacks?

Q3   The UK has gone to war against Iraq twice in recent years, in 1991 and 2003.

    a)   Write a short paragraph describing the events leading up to the 1991 war against Iraq, based on the phrases in the box below.

invasion of Kuwait	UN sanctions	15 January 1991	US-led coalition

    b)   Write a short paragraph describing the events leading up to the 2003 war against Iraq, based on the phrases in the box below.

UN weapons inspectors	UN Security Council wanted to give Iraq more time to cooperate	weapons of mass destruction	Saddam Hussein had been uncooperative for twelve years already

DISCUSSION QUESTION Q4   Richer members of the UN aim to give 0.7% of their GNP to the World Bank and similar organisations to provide funds for development in poorer countries.

Do you think 0.7% is enough? Should we cut back on services in this country to help poorer countries even more?

DISCUSSION QUESTION Q5   Many people in the UK still feel that the 2003 invasion of Iraq to remove Saddam Hussein was largely justified.

When is a war justified?
Discuss this question in a group and note down the main opinions.

War is always messy, but sometimes necessary...

It's a sad reflection on humanity that we sometimes have to resort to military action to resolve situations. But sometimes it can be the only option. Worth reflecting on for a moment or two...

What is the Law?

Q1　Rewrite this statement in everyday English, keeping it as brief as possible.

> Law is a formal method of controlling people and society through rules set down and then enforced through courts and the legal system.

Q2　Answer these questions on the way the law helps society to run smoothly.

a)　For each of these four statements give a real-life example from recent events in the UK.

> *Laws apply equally to all members of society.*
> *Laws prevent people from doing dangerous things.*
> *Laws try to stop people from harming each other.*
> *Laws protect people's rights.*

> It can be something that happened locally or something that made the national news.

> Think about tax, crime, education... and anything else that springs to mind.

b)　It's often said that a society without laws would collapse into chaos. What do you think would happen in this country if all the laws were abolished tomorrow? Write a mini-essay describing what might happen.

Q3　Give a brief definition for each of these types of law.

a)　case law

b)　statute law

c)　delegated law

d)　European law

DISCUSSION QUESTION Q4　A statue of 'Justice' on the roof of the Old Bailey in London shows a woman wearing a blindfold and holding a pair of scales.

What do you think the statue is saying about justice?

DISCUSSION QUESTION Q5　Read this extract from a newspaper report.

> **TAKING THE LAW INTO HIS OWN HANDS**
> In August 1999 the Norfolk farmer Tony Martin shot and killed a sixteen year old and injured an older man who were attempting to burgle his farm. The farm had been burgled several times in the past and Mr. Martin lived out of earshot of his neighbours' homes.

Tony Martin was convicted for murder, but the conviction was reduced to manslaughter and he was released in 2003.

Discuss this case and try to decide whether or not he was right to take the law into his own hands. Give reasons for your final decision.

Crime

Q1 For each of a) to f), write down whether it is a crime.

    a) Shoplifting

    b) Driving at 34 m.p.h through a 30 m.p.h speed limit area

    c) Racial harassment

    d) Eating pork if you're Jewish, or beef if you're Hindu

    e) Downloading pornographic pictures of children from the internet

    f) Committing adultery

Q2 Explain what's wrong with this statement.

> I saw a documentary about these computer hackers. They transferred over a million pounds from a bank into their own accounts. No one got hurt but they were sent to prison. It seems really unfair.

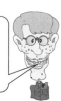

Q3 Match up each crime described below with the best description from the box.

> kleptomania   motive of personal financial gain
>
> a crime of passion   motive of revenge

    a) A man catches his wife in bed with someone else and kills them both there and then.

    b) A bank clerk uses false accounts to swindle money from his employers.

    c) A woman deliberately sets fire to a building owned by the manager who sacked her.

    d) Someone repeatedly shoplifts small items from shops and can't stop themselves doing it.

DISCUSSION QUESTION Q4 People in desperate situations can feel like committing a crime's the only way out.

Can you imagine any situations in which someone might be tempted to commit a crime out of desperation?

Crime

Q1   Each of these organisations helps victims of crime. Use your general knowledge or do some research to find out what each one does and write it down.

a)   Victim Support

b)   Criminal Injuries Compensation Authority

c)   Refuge

d)   Support After Murder and Manslaughter

e)   Brake

f)   Survivors UK

g)   Lifeline

Q2   For each type of crime listed below describe what the effects could be on the people directly involved and the community as a whole.

a)   burglaries on local homes

b)   vandalism in the park

c)   burning abandoned cars and rubbish

d)   muggings in the street

e)   letting off fireworks in a dangerous way

f)   selling alcohol to underage drinkers

g)   buying and taking drugs

...and 20 Silk Cut.

 Q3   Has anyone in your group been a victim of crime?

Ask them what happened and how it made them feel.

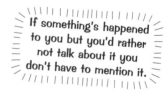
If something's happened to you but you'd rather not talk about it you don't have to mention it.

 Q4   In Iran, the law says that the family of a murderer has to pay a large sum of money to the victim's family as compensation.

Do you think this would help victims' families feel better?
Write a list of pros and cons for this system.

Wearing really smelly aftershave should be a crime...

...and wearing dodgy earphones so everyone on the bus can just hear a crackly bass line. And spitting in the street. And showing your bum crack. I can't be the only person who doesn't like it.

Tackling Crime

Q1   Explain what each of these different types of police officer does.

    a)   'bobby on the beat'

    b)   officers in patrol cars

    c)   detectives

    d)   forensic scientists

    e)   police psychologists

    f)   crowd control officers

Q2   In recent years the Government has broadcast several advertisements warning the public about the dangers of speeding and drink-driving.

    a)   Describe an advertisement which you found memorable.

    b)   Do you think this advertisement would have had an effect on drivers' behaviour? Explain your answer.

Q3   Choose the most likely punishment for each of these crimes from the box.

    a)   Being in possession of a small amount of cannabis.

    b)   Vandalising gravestones.

    c)   Armed robbery of a village post office.

    d)   Premeditated murder.

> life imprisonment
>
> 8 years in prison
>
> community service

Q4   "The kind of people who mug old ladies are hardly likely to turn up to a youth club with a dodgy pool table and some cans of fizzy drinks."

What do you think is the best way to get young people to steer clear of crime? Come up with a list of ideas.

Hello, hello, hello...

I wonder if in all the history of policing there's ever been a policeman who actually said that.
Maybe one who was meeting three of his mates at the pub...

British Justice System

Q1 Are the following cases subject to criminal law or civil law?

   a) A company does not fulfil its contract to supply goods on time.

   b) A soldier appears at the Old Bailey charged with murder.

   c) A best-selling author sues a tabloid newspaper for libel.

   d) A woman sues her employer for unfair dismissal.

   e) A motorist is fined at the Magistrates Court for exceeding the speed limit.

Q2 Copy out these sentences and fill in the blanks with the words from the box.

life	police	jury	judge	guilty	defendant
appeal	Magistrates		Crown	remand	

Hugh Dunnit was arrested by the .... in possession of a firearm. He was

brought before the local .... Court and charged with murder. A date was set for

his trial at the .... Court several months later. Meanwhile, Hugh was placed on

.... At his trial Hugh, the ...., was found .... by a

.... He was sentenced to .... imprisonment by the

.... Now Hugh's defence counsel is working on his ....

Q3 Copy out this table and fill in the gaps.

Questions	Criminal Law	Civil Law
Who Brings the case?	Crown Prosecution Service	
Who makes the decision?		Usually judges
How is the verdict given?		Liable/Not liable
Types of punishment?	Fine / probation / curfews / community service / prison	

Q4 Look up 'Courts' in your local Yellow Pages. Write down the name of each court in your area, then write down what kind of cases each one hears.

Q5 The law is like the Ritz Hotel — open to everyone.

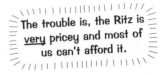

The trouble is, the Ritz is <u>very</u> pricey and most of us can't afford it.

Bringing a civil action can be very expensive by the time you've paid lawyers' fees and costs and some people can't afford it. Do you think this is fair? Is this "justice for all"?

How Laws Affect Young People

Q1 As you get older it becomes legal to do more things. Write down how old you have to be before you can legally do each of the things in the box.

buy lottery tickets	buy alcohol	work part-time	drive a car	stand for Parliament
have heterosexual sex	buy cigarettes	buy fireworks	adopt a child	have homosexual sex (males)
vote in elections	get married without parental consent	go into a casino	buy soft drinks in a bar	make a will

Q2 Read this article about joyriding then answer the questions below.

DEADLY JOYRIDERS WILL GET FOURTEEN YEARS

Residents on a Belfast housing estate welcomed proposals to increase the maximum penalty for causing the death of another person while in charge of a motor vehicle to fourteen years.

The estate has been plagued with joyriding over the summer, with burnt out and wrecked cars littering the estate.

The joyriders' spree has also resulted in two deaths. A 15 year old boy and an 8 year old girl were killed when the boy lost control of the stolen car which he was driving and swerved on to a pavement,

hitting Susy MacMahon.

Her father Jackie, 32, says he would like to see the proposals go even further. "This lad killed my daughter. Murderers can be put away for life. Why shouldn't it be the same for joyriders who kill people with their stupid, selfish behaviour?"

a) Why does Jackie MacMahon think the punishments should be even harsher?

b) Joyriding can lead to accidents and fatalities. What other effects can joyriding have on a community? Use the article and your own ideas.

 Q3 "Young people from poorer, socially deprived areas are more likely to commit crimes than young people from better off areas."

Suggest reasons why this might be true.

 Q4 "Sometimes breaking the law is fun."

Think of as many examples as you can of young people breaking the law 'for kicks'. Do you think it's worth it?

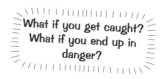
What if you get caught? What if you end up in danger?

Do you have any proof of your age, Mr. Bond...

The laws about not buying booze before you're 18 and fags before you're 16 get broken a lot. Bear in mind that the laws aren't just there to spoil your fun — they're supposed to protect your health.

How Laws Affect Young People

Q1   Put these stages in order so they describe what could happen to a young offender.

Case heard at Magistrates Court.	Sent to youth detention centre on remand.	Case heard at Crown Court.
Arrested on suspicion of assault.	Offender is convicted and sentenced.	Charged with assault.
	Offender goes back to youth detention centre.	Offender released from detention with life-long criminal record.

Q2   Explain what each of these people do.

    a)   youth panel magistrate

    b)   defence lawyer

    c)   justices' clerk

Q3   Explain what happens to someone who gets each of these.

    a)   community service

    b)   fine

    c)   prison sentence

    d)   caution

 Q4   76% of young male prisoners under the age of 21 reoffend within two years of release.

Do you think prison is an effective punishment for young people?
What alternative approaches are there?

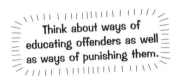

Think about ways of educating offenders as well as ways of punishing them.

DISCUSSION QUESTION   Q5   If a young person (under 18) gets a criminal record it sticks for 2½ years for minor offences, and can last for life if the conviction was for a violent crime.

    a)   What problems could this cause for an offender?

    b)   What benefits are there for the rest of society?

Proceed with caution...

All these questions one after another make it sound like young people are all foaming at the mouth, desperate to rush around committing crimes. I know you're not like that. You're lovely.

The Law and Your Rights

Q1   Fill in the gaps using words from the box.

You can be arrested for refusing to give a police officer your ....

You don't have to answer police questions before you've had ....

Anyone under 17 who's held by the police should have .... with them during interviews.

If the police search you they have to give you a .... of the search and explain why they did it.

The police can usually hold suspected criminals for 24 hours but for suspected .... it's even longer.

While you're in police custody being interviewed you're entitled to ....

meal breaks	written record	telephone number	name and address
an appropriate adult	a childminder	criminal record	cigarette breaks
legal advice	terrorists	clean clothes	arsonists

Q2   Use the internet or newspaper archives at your library to find out about a recent case where there has been an appeal and a conviction has been overturned.

a)   What was the original conviction?

b)   How long did the defendant or defendants spend in prison?

c)   Why was the conviction overturned?

What do you mean —
I look suspicious?

 Q3   The police are not supposed to stop people unless they have a good reason for it. Read these statements.

(1) "I know I look pretty scruffy, but that doesn't mean I'm a drug dealer. I've been stopped by the police more times than I can remember."

(2) "I've been in the police for over 20 years and I reckon you can tell when someone's up to no good, just by looking at them."

(3) "If people don't want to be suspected of crimes they haven't committed then it's up to them to dress and behave in a normal, respectable way."

Talk about each statement and write down your ideas.

You have the right to remain in bed on a Saturday...

It's not very likely that any of this will ever affect you personally but it's still a good idea to know what's what and what your rights are if you are arrested. Just in case.

Politics and Democracy

Q1 The UK has a democratically elected government.

a) Copy out the paragraph below, filling the gaps with words from the box.

democracy	members	Opposition	vote	elect	Commons	Government

The UK is a .... where we .... representatives — Members of Parliament (MPs)

to run the country. The political party that will form the .... is chosen in a general election.

These take place every 4-5 years. Everyone over 18 can .... In a general election, the

party with the most elected MPs wins the election. The runner-up party becomes the ....

All MPs sit in the House of .... where they debate issues and pass laws.

b) In your own words, explain what a democracy is.

Q2 In general elections in the UK over a quarter of eligible people don't usually bother to vote.

Below are the views of four people who have chosen not to vote.
For each one, write a few sentences persuading them to use their vote.

1 "I'm not interested in politics so there's no point in voting."

2 "All the parties have pretty much the same policies, so it doesn't really matter who gets into power."

3 "There's no point in voting because once politicians get into power they don't do what you want anyway."

4 "I don't really understand what they're talking about, so it isn't right that I should vote."

DISCUSSION QUESTION **Q3** In Australia you can be fined if you don't turn up to vote.

Would this be a good way of getting more people to vote in the UK? Discuss reasons for and against making voting compulsory.

Try to come up with at least two points for and two against. Then decide if you're for or against it.

DISCUSSION QUESTION **Q4** Not all countries have a democratic government.

Discuss the benefits of living in a democracy.
Can you think of any drawbacks?

Think of countries you know which don't have democracies. How are things different for the people in these countries?

I reckon politics is boring — lets have a vote on it...

Politics has a huge impact on everyone's lives. If you want to get more involved, have a look at government websites, or find out about the UK Youth Parliament.

Politics in the UK

Q1 Which of the following do you need to vote in the UK?

> be 21 or over   British citizenship
>
> British driving licence   name on the electoral register

Q2 Say whether each of these statements is true or false.
Rewrite any false statements to make them true.

   a) Voting takes place at local polling stations.

   b) Voting is by public ballot, so you know how each person has voted.

   c) Elected MPs go to Parliament to help make laws and run the country's affairs.

Q3 The main UK political parties have fairly 'central' political ideas.
But some are more right or left wing than others.

   a) Name the 3 main political parties in the UK and say whether each is more right or left wing.

   b) Name 3 minority political parties in the UK.

   c) Look at the comments below, and say if they are usually
associated with right or left wing politics.

> Government shouldn't interfere in business unless it really has to.

> We should share out our wealth as evenly as we can.

> Maintaining strict law and order is extremely important.

> People shouldn't get things just because of who they are or how much money they have.

Q4 Parliamentary candidates nearly always represent a political party.
Independents can stand in elections but are rarely elected.

Discuss reasons why people stand as independent candidates.

Q5 In 2001 the general election put 539 men and 120
women into Parliament. Only 9 black MPs were elected.

What do you think the government could do to make
women and ethnic minorities better represented?

General Elections

Q1 Choose the best ending for each sentence and write it out.

   a) **A political party's manifesto is…**
   b) **Canvassing takes place locally using…**
   c) **National media is used for…**

   i)   party political broadcasts.
   ii) a document outlining their policies.
   iii) various publicity materials, posters, flyers, etc.

Q2 Write out this paragraph, filling the gaps with words from the box.

   The UK is divided up into 659 voting areas known as .... Each area is
   supposed to have roughly equal numbers of .... — there are around 70,000
   in each one. At a .... voters in each area can choose between a number of
   .... — usually one from each of the main .... and a few others.
   Whoever gets the most votes wins a .... in Parliament.

   | candidates | voters | seat | general election | constituencies | parties |

Q3 Explain how the first-past-the-post system works
    when electing Members of Parliament.

 Q4 General elections in the UK are often described as a 'two horse' race.

   Discuss what this means. Write down as many advantages and disadvantages
   of elections being a 'two horse race' as you can think of.

 Q5 In 1969 the voting age in the UK was lowered to 18 years.
    Today some people want it reduced to 16.

   Come up with three reasons for the proposal and three
   against it then decide your own opinion.

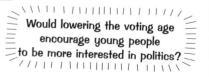

Would lowering the voting age
encourage young people
to be more interested in politics?

Are they canvassing, or just putting up a tent...

Political parties use 'spin doctors' to help them present a positive image to the public. Have a look
at different types of media and find different examples of how politicians get their message across.

National Government

Q1 Parliament is made up of three parts — name each bit and write a short sentence to describe it.

Q2 Copy out the sentences below, filling the blanks with words from the box.

Parliament is the .... part of government — it makes the laws. The .... is a .... forum for MPs where they discuss national and .... issues. Inside the House members sit with their political party — Government one side, ... on the other.

Opposition	House of Commons	legislative	debating	international

Q3 Part of your MP's job is to help protect your rights as an individual.

If you complained to your MP that you had waited two years for an important operation what could he or she do for you?

DISCUSSION QUESTION Q4 Who's who in Parliament...

Write down as many names and/or job titles of people in Government as you can think of.

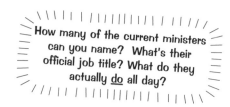

How many of the current ministers can you name? What's their official job title? What do they actually <u>do</u> all day?

DISCUSSION QUESTION Q5 Hold your own election. First divide into three groups — each group's a political party.

- Choose one person to be your candidate.

- Write a manifesto.

- Choose a name for your party and a punchy election slogan for your party.

- Write a speech for your candidate to deliver to the class.

- When all the candidates have made their speeches to the whole class, hold a secret ballot and appoint a returning officer to read the result.

Tony Blair is in the House...

The House of Lords has been going through all sorts of changes the last few years but it still does the same basic job — it's a kind of counter-balance to the party politics in the House of Commons.

Regional Government

Q1   Choose the right definition from the box for each word or phrase below.

a)   centralised government

b)   referendum

c)   devolution

d)   regional assembly

> when the people vote on an issue, not for a person or party
>
> regional equivalent of Parliament
>
> moving power away from central government
>
> when a country is ruled entirely from one centre of government

Q2   The table below shows election results for 3 political parties in 3 made-up constituencies.

	Hayfield	Cartington	Dunghill East	Total Votes
Free Beer Party	20	40	20	80
Old Fogey Party	2	15	20	37
Miserable Bureaucrats Party	30	15	30	75
Winner (First Past the Post)	MB	Free Beer	MB	

a)   Under the 'first past the post system' used in UK national elections, which party would form the government if results were like this across the country?

b)   Which party actually got the most votes?

c)   What would happen if proportional representation was used for this election with one seat in Parliament being awarded for every 40 votes?

d)   How would this change the overall results of the election?

DISCUSSION QUESTION

Q3   Proportional representation is used in UK regional assembly elections.

Many of the smaller UK parties support the use of proportional representation in general elections, but Labour and the Conservatives are against the idea.

Why do you think this is?

> Your answers to Q2 will help you answer this one...

DISCUSSION QUESTION

Q4   In 1997 Tony Blair's New Labour government began a programme of devolution in the UK, giving greater powers to Scotland, Wales and Northern Ireland.

Discuss the arguments for and against devolution.
Do you think it should be extended to regions of England, e.g. the North East?

Local Government

Q1   Copy out this paragraph, filling the blanks with words from the box.

Britain is divided into areas, each with its own .... or .... council.

These local authorities exist to provide local .... Delivering at the point of need is

more .... People can .... more fully in local affairs and help to build a

better .... Local councillors are .... just like MPs.

> community   services   participate   metropolitan
>
> county   efficient   elected

Q2   Local councils provide a lot of important services to the community.

a)   Write down all the services from the box that are provided by local councils.

> fire service   hospitals   waste collection   tourism
>
> prison service   libraries   trading standards   driving tests

b)   List three more services that local councils provide.

Q3   Local authorities get the money to pay for services
from two different sources. What are they?

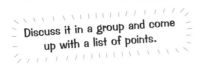 Q4   Local councillors stand for election just like MPs but they don't get paid.

Discuss it in a group and come up with a list of points.

What do you think motivates someone
to stand for election as a local councillor?

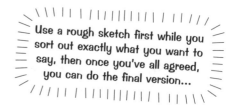 Q5   Councils deal with local issues like education, recycling, leisure and transport.

What do you think are the main issues in
your local area? Work in a group to create
an A4 leaflet showing which issues concern
you most and what you would change if
you were elected to the local council.

Use a rough sketch first while you sort out exactly what you want to say, then once you've all agreed, you can do the final version...

Local authorities are for local people...

Local councils don't exactly get to deal with the fun stuff. Waste collection, the library bus and
planning regulations aren't most people's idea of a roaring good time, but it's all dead useful.

The European Parliament

Q1   How often are Members of the European Parliament (MEPs) elected?
      Write down the correct answer from the box.

> every 6 seconds   every 4 years   every 5 years
> never, they're appointed by the prime minister

Q2   Each member state of the EU has a different number of MEPs.

      Explain why this is.

Q3   The European Parliament has limited powers. Read the sentences below and
      decide if they're true or false. Rewrite the false sentences to make them true.

      a) MEPs discuss proposals made by the European Commission.

      b) The European Commission has to accept changes recommended by the European Parliament.

      c) The European Parliament jointly controls the EU budget with the Council of Ministers.

      d) The European Parliament meets in Dusseldorf.

Q4   You're a European citizen, and you have the right to make your opinions heard.

      Find out who your MEP is, and what sort of issues
      they are raising at the European Parliament.
      What else would you like them to deal with?

      *You could try using the internet to find out this stuff...
      or you could phone your local council and ask for information.*

DISCUSSION QUESTION Q5   "The UK would do much better if it left the EU."

      Discuss what positive and negative effects there could be if we did decide to leave.

DISCUSSION QUESTION Q6   More states are joining the European Union. This process is called enlargement.

      How do you see Europe developing in your lifetime?
      Discuss ideas as a group, then write a mini-essay
      describing the future of Europe.

      *If we became more closely linked
      to Europe, how would it affect
      ordinary people's lives?*

      *Do you think we'll ever join the euro?
      How would this affect Britain and Europe's economy?*

      Mmm... red wine.

      Mmm... warm beer.

The National Economy

Q1   Write a one-sentence definition of an economy, using all the words and phrases from the box.

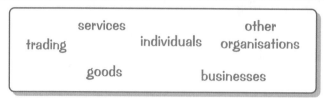

services
trading   individuals   other organisations
goods   businesses

Q2   Answer these questions on the UK economy.

a)   Write down the correct name for each type of economy described below.
Choose your answers from the words on the right.

> All the goods and services available are supplied by businesses.

MIXED

FREE MARKET

> Some decisions are taken by the government and some are left up to businesses.

b)   The UK has a mixed economy. Write down two real life examples of products or services supplied by businesses and two examples of products or services supplied by the government.

Q3   These questions are all about the Chancellor of the Exchequer.

a)   Who appoints the Chancellor of the Exchequer?

b)   Describe the Chancellor's job in as much detail as you can.

**WANTED
BIG CHEESE**
Must like:
Red boxes
Big sums
Living next door
to the Prime Minister

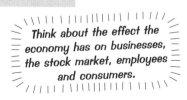

Q4   The Bank of England uses interest rates to control spending and inflation.
Copy out the charts below and fill in the blanks.

a)
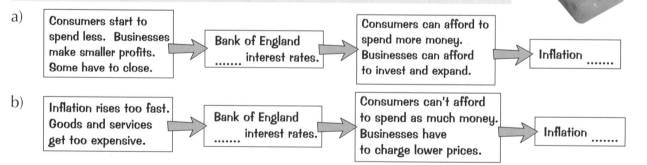

| Consumers start to spend less. Businesses make smaller profits. Some have to close. | → | Bank of England .... interest rates. | → | Consumers can afford to spend more money. Businesses can afford to invest and expand. | → | Inflation .... |

b)

| Inflation rises too fast. Goods and services get too expensive. | → | Bank of England .... interest rates. | → | Consumers can't afford to spend as much money. Businesses have to charge lower prices. | → | Inflation .... |

DISCUSSION QUESTION **Q5**   When Bill Clinton was campaigning to become President of the USA one of his most famous slogans was "It's the economy, stupid."

Why is the economy so important to voters?

Think about the effect the economy has on businesses, the stock market, employees and consumers.

Tax

Q1   Decide whether each of the following statements is true or false.
Rewrite any false statements to make them true.

    a)   Parliament has to approve the Government's budget before it goes into effect.

    b)   The Government pays for public services using money raised through customs tax.

    c)   The Public Works Committee makes sure that the government is spending
all the money raised through taxation properly.

    d)   There are several different indirect taxes in this country,
and every adult must pay all of them.

Q2   The two main types of taxes are direct and indirect taxes.

    a)   Give an example of a direct tax.

    b)   Give an example of an indirect tax.

From **The Tax Collector's Manual***:*
Lesson 4 — Staying awake at work.

Q3   Corporation tax is a tax paid on profits by business organisations. If there was a big rise
in the UK rate of corporation tax, what effects could this have on each of the following?

    a)   government income in the short-term

    b)   businesses

    c)   government income in the long-term

Q4   Write down as many public services as you can think of that are paid for with taxes.

DISCUSSION QUESTION Q5   The government spends millions of pounds every year on schools, hospitals,
defence and other services. This has to be paid for out of taxation.

    In your group discuss:
should there be more taxation to make these services better **or**
should the government encourage more private sector involvement
in these areas to reduce taxation.

DISCUSSION QUESTION Q6   In most countries higher earners pay a higher rate of tax.
But governments are careful not to tax high earners too much.

    Do you think it is fair that higher earners should pay a higher rate of tax?
What are governments afraid will happen if high earners are charged too much tax?

Business and Enterprise

Q1 Draw a table with two columns and title them 'Public sector organisations' and 'Private sector organisations'. Write out each description from the box under the correct heading.

Owned by the government	Aim to make a profit	British Airways	Army
NHS	Supermarket	Privately owned	Don't make a profit

Q2 When private businesses do well it makes the whole economy healthier.

a) Arrange these boxes in a sensible order to show how success in one part of the economy helps other parts. Start with "Go Away Holidays opens a new call centre."

Go Away Holidays opens a new call centre.

New employees spend money in local area e.g. going out, shopping, etc....

Local business owners take on more staff.

New staff at local businesses can afford to spend more.

Local businesses, e.g. cafés, shops, cinemas get more trade.

Employs 100 people.

b) All companies pay a tax on profits called Corporation Tax. Explain how this helps the public sector.

c) Explain why governments often give tax breaks or subsidies to companies setting up in areas with high unemployment.

Q3 Ben's Buns make cream buns for the big supermarket chains. They plan to open a new factory.

a) What raw materials will the factory need?

b) What staff will the factory need?

c) What transport needs will the factory have — how are they going to get the buns to the shops?

d) Bearing in mind your answers for a)-c) suggest some suitable locations for the new factory.

DISCUSSION QUESTION Q4 Local businesses have a big effect on the local economy.

Talk about businesses in your area and what difference they make.

Have any big businesses opened or closed recently in your area?

What are the main businesses? How many people do they employ?

Pants for giants — that's big business for you...

People tend to think of business as all about profits, but setting up a business isn't just good for the owners — it is really good for the national economy and local people too.

Business and the Economy

Q1   Write out the following sentences and fill in the blanks using the words given below.

selling	value	investment	success
dividend	shares	investors	profit

You'll have to use one of the words more than once.

Shareholders are .... in a company. They hope to get a return on their .... in two ways — by getting a good .... (a share of the profit) and by .... their shares at a higher price.

A company's .... is measured by the .... of its shares and the amount of .... it makes. Companies raise money for future .... by selling more .... in the company to investors.

Q2   Explain why dealing in stocks and shares can be a risky business.

Q3   Draw a table with two columns and title them BOOM and RECESSION.

a)   Write everything from the box that describes a boom in the "boom" column.

b)   Write everything from the box that describes a recession in the "recession" column.

boom economy = one that is doing really well
economy in recession = one that is doing really badly

Consumer spending rises	Share prices go up	House prices go up
Consumers spend less		New businesses open
Shareholders get low dividends	Unemployment	Businesses close down
No new investment in business		Resources lying idle, e.g. closed factories
Share prices fall	House prices fall	Investment in business rises

 Q4   House prices have risen so much in the UK that many young people can't afford to buy their own homes.

Discuss how the government could help to ease this problem.

 Q5   Stock markets are an essential part of the world economy, but they can be affected by world events.

Following the terrorist attacks on Washington and New York on 11 September 2001 there was a drop in share prices all around the world.

In a group try to explain why this happened.

A bare market — no one can afford to buy clothes...

Great Uncle Noah always used to say "What goes up, must come down," and "The higher the return the greater the risk." Old and tired sayings, maybe, but very very true if you're talking about shares.

Your Part in the Economy

Q1 When you are older you will almost certainly have to work to earn an income. The box below lists different things you can do with your money. Give a real life example for each one.

> spend   save   donate   invest

Q2 What would you use each of the following financial products for?

a) current account

b) overdraft facility

c) ISA

d) credit card

e) loan

f) mortgage

g) pension scheme

DISCUSSION QUESTION **Q3** There are all sorts of places where you can get financial advice, some good, some bad.

Make a list of different sources of financial advice.
Rate each one with one star, two stars or three for how
useful you think the advice is and explain each rating.

DISCUSSION QUESTION **Q4** Read these statements about internet banking and shopping.

> *"I'd never give out my card details on the internet — you never know who might get hold of them."*

> *"Internet banking and shopping is no more dodgy than banking or shopping on the High Street."*

a) Which statement do people in your group agree with more?

b) Write a set of guidelines for young people using the internet for banking and shopping.

DISCUSSION QUESTION **Q5** The best way to stay on top of your spending is to set yourself a budget (and stick to it).

a) Write down your monthly income from jobs and pocket money and a rough estimate of what you spend on things like food, transport, clothes and going out each month.

b) Suggest ways for other people in your group to save money.

c) Use the group's suggestions to set your own budget for next month.

At least you don't have to write the national budget...

Personal finance is a minefield — there are scary numbers of people out there after your money.
Get money-wise and learn how to look after your own cash if you want to avoid the scams.

Global Economy

Q1 Most countries in the world are tied into the global economy through trade links.

a) Write a definition for each of these terms.

> LEDC   colony   MEDC   Raw material   NICs

b) Copy out these paragraphs and fill in the gaps using words from the box on the right.

Some of the trading patterns in the world today reflect those from
.... times. LEDCs tend to produce .... materials and
MEDCs turn these in to .... goods.

There are other reasons that can affect an **LEDC's** abilities to develop. For
example war and .... instability have made it difficult for some
countries to develop fully.

However some countries have been able to .... from LEDCs to
MEDCs. South East Asian countries such as Singapore and Taiwan are now
known as **NICs** (Newly Industrialised Countries). Many of them provided a cheap
.... for the **USA** and Japan, but they now produce high-tech goods.

> trade
> manufactured   coffee
> political   prices   raw
> market   tea   colonial
> work force
> develop

Q2 Write out these boxes in the correct order to explain how
the debts of many LEDCs have become unmanageable.

> LEDCs can't afford to pay back
> their loans. Any money they have
> goes on paying off the interest.

> LEDCs borrow money at low interest
> rates, planning to invest it in
> building up trade and industry.

> Interest rates climb massively in
> the 1980s — the amount of money
> LEDCs owe grows and grows.

> LEDCs have no money to spend on basic services like schools
> and healthcare. An unhealthy uneducated workforce can't
> improve the economy and the country gets even poorer.

 Q3 Read this extract from an article published on a charity website in 2002.

> The 2015 Millennium Development Goal of halving
> the number of people suffering extreme poverty, will not
> be met without total cancellation of the debts of the
> world's poorest and most indebted countries. This is the
> stark conclusion of a new study launched today, on the
> eve of this year's meeting of G7 finance ministers, and
> as Tony Blair starts a tour of African countries.

Do you think it is sensible for LEDCs
to have all their debts cancelled or is
it 'money for nothing'?
Make notes of your discussion and
turn them into a mini-essay looking
at all the different points of view.

World Trade

Q1 These questions are all about multinational companies. Enjoy.

    a) What is a multinational company?

    b) Give <u>two</u> reasons why a multinational would base parts of its business in poorer countries.

    c) Write down <u>two</u> benefits of multinationals for the host country.

    d) Why do some people think that the host countries don't get a fair deal.

Q2 Copy out this extract from a Fair Trade leaflet, and fill the blanks with words from the box.

> trade   unfair share   poor   producers
>
> Fair Trade   small farmers   improve

Millions of people around the world depend on global

.... Many are .... or plantation workers

who are .... because they receive an ....

of the benefits of trade.

.... is an alternative approach that aims to

.... the livelihoods and well-being of ....

by improving market access and paying a better price.

...mmm, fairly traded corpse. More ethical <u>and</u> tastier.

DISCUSSION QUESTION **Q3** A Ghanaian cocoa farmer gets 1.2% of the price we pay for a bar of chocolate.

- Do you think a director of a multinational company selling chocolate bars would think this is fair? Why?

- Do you think a Ghanaian farmer would think this is fair? Why?

- What do you think?

DISCUSSION QUESTION **Q4** Many of the things we buy come from abroad. The choices we make can affect businesses and employees in other countries.

Make a list of things you buy regularly and talk about where they come from.
Who makes money as a result of your purchases?

Think about what you drink, eat, wear, do for entertainment...

Money makes the world go round, or so they say...

The world's best selling book is the Bible but more people in the world recognise the Coca-Cola logo than recognise a cross. These multinational organisations really do have a massive effect.

Environmental Issues

Q1   These statements are all about threats to the environment. Say whether each one is true or false.

a) Oxygen is a greenhouse gas.

b) Greenhouse gases are produced when fossil fuels are burnt.

c) Sulphur dioxide and nitrogen oxide, released when fossil fuels are
    burnt, mix with water vapour in the air to form harmless alkaline rain.

d) Population increase puts more pressure on natural habitats.

e) An oil spill is very dangerous to fish but birds and
    sea mammals are not usually affected.

Q2   Do some research on the internet or in your library to find a recent
      example of each of the environmental problems listed below.

industrial pollution
e.g. chemical spill

species in danger
of extinction

habitat destruction
e.g. deforestation

Write a short paragraph about each one.

Q3   A local radio station has given you a five-minute slot to talk about the environment.
      Write a short talk persuading local drivers to leave their cars at home and find other
      methods of transport to get to work.

DISCUSSION
QUESTION   Q4   Greenpeace attract a lot of attention to environmental issues by organising
                  dramatic demonstrations, e.g. sailing alongside ships carrying polluting chemicals.

Make a list of different ways of campaigning on environmental
issues and decide which one you think is most effective.

DISCUSSION
QUESTION   Q5   Read this statement.

What do you think?

Global warming is nowhere near the biggest threat to mankind.
War, poverty, disease and famine are still
much greater threats to this and future generations.
In any case, all the predicted effects of global warming are
entirely manageable — there is no impending disaster.

International Action

Q1 In 1992 a UN Earth Summit was held in Rio de Janeiro.

   a)   What was the name of the agreement signed by world leaders at this Earth Summit?

   b)   Briefly outline what this agreement said.

Q2 Copy out the passage below choosing the correct word from each pair in brackets.

The 1997 (Kyoto Protocol / Rio Protocol) was chiefly concerned with (greenhouse / oxygen) gas emissions. The Protocol aimed to commit individual countries to (increasing / reducing) emissions by set targets based on (1990 / 1909) emission levels. Developing countries were (given greater / exempt from) emissions targets as they'd historically been responsible for (most / a fraction) of the world emissions. Many countries signed the agreement, including the (EU / UN). However some of the "big" countries such as the USA, Russia and Australia chose not to sign. They said that emissions cuts would damage economic (growth / recession) and this would (speed up / slow down) the development of environmentally friendly technology. The USA wanted the Protocol to look more at other ways of reducing greenhouse gas levels such as (tree-planting / CO_2 removal factories).

Q3 The Kyoto Protocol identified six gases produced around the world as "greenhouse gases". The lesser known ones are CH_4, N_2O, HFCs, PFCs and SF_6.

   a)   Pick out the main greenhouse gas from the list below.

   > O_3 HCl CO_2 H_2O NH_3

   b)   Give two ways that countries produce the gas named in a).

   c)   Suggest two ways for a country to reduce the levels of this gas in its atmosphere.

Q4 India is one of the world's biggest countries. Industry and the economy are expanding rapidly but there are still many people who live in deep poverty.

Why do you think India is reluctant to cut greenhouse gas emissions?

DISCUSSION QUESTION **Q5** What role can each of these play in dealing with environmental problems?

   • Governments?
   • Individuals?
   • Businesses and industries?

It's not just a lot of hot air...

Even though it was put together in 1997, the Kyoto Protocol still hasn't come into effect as it needs more big emissions producers to sign up. In the meantime, don't forget to recycle your bottles.

Sustainable Development

Q1   Write down a brief definition of sustainable development.

Q2   Conserving resources is a big part of sustainable development.
Suggest a way of protecting each of the following:

a)   fossil fuels like coal, oil and gas

b)   clean water

c)   fish stocks in the oceans

d)   forests

e)   clean air

f)   farm land

Q3   Agenda 21 is an action plan for dealing with problems facing the world at a global level.

a)   According to Agenda 21 there are four main problems facing the world. What are they?

b)   Which of these is an Agenda 21 slogan?

| _Do something now._ | _Think globally, act locally._ | _Actions speak louder than words._ | _Not in my backyard._ |

c)   About 170 countries have signed up to Agenda 21 but several countries have not.
Do you think the Agenda can make a difference if all countries don't get involved?

 Q4   In Local Agenda 21, local authorities were asked to make
plans for dealing with a number of environmental issues.

a)   Find out what your local council is doing for Local Agenda 21.

b)   What else could councils do to aid sustainable development? Come up with at
least three things your council could do to be more environmentally friendly.

c)   List at least three things you could you do to make your lifestyle more
environmentally friendly.

 Q5   We are currently using the world's resources at a greater rate than they can be replaced.
This means there may not be enough resources for future generations to use.

What factors stand in the way of sustainable development?
Do you think sustainable development is possible?
Write down your thoughts.

Agenda 21 — not the catchiest of titles...

Some people think all this talk about the world running out of important resources is scaremongering.
Other people are really, really scared. Look into the facts and make up your own mind.

Producing the News

Q1 There are more types of media today than ever before.

a) Write a list of as many different types of media as you can which cover the news.

b) For each of your answers to a) give an example of an actual channel or publication.

c) For each of your answers to b) describe what kind of news it covers.

Q2 News stories can have local, national or global importance.

a) Draw a table like the one below and put each of the news stories from the box under the right heading.

LOCAL NEWS	NATIONAL NEWS	GLOBAL NEWS

> supermarket chain goes bust   rail crash
>
> theft of a car   G8 summit   ring road plans
>
> interest rate cut   famine in Africa   teachers go on strike

b) Pick two stories from your 'national news' column in part a) and imagine they're being covered by a local paper. Make up headlines to show how the local paper might tackle them.

Q3 Lots of different people work on the news. Explain what each of the people below does.

newspaper editor   reporter   paparazzo   photojournalist

DISCUSSION QUESTION Q4 The average person watches 28 hours of television each week.

Do you think watching TV is the best way to get informed about local, national and global events?

In your discussion compare TV with all the alternative ways of finding out news.

DISCUSSION QUESTION Q5 'Whistleblowers' reveal confidential information about the organisations they work for to the press.

What arguments are there for and against whistleblowing?

And finally...

If you want to get a really good overall picture of what's going on you need to read at least one paper a day, listen to the radio and watch **TV** news. Doesn't leave time for much else though.

Freedom of Speech

Q1   For each sentence below choose the best word from each pair.

a)   A free press is more common in a **democracy/dictatorship**.

b)   In some countries governments **sensationalise/censor**
newspapers to make sure they don't say anything too critical.

c)   A government which practises censorship can use the media
to **control/report** the opinions of their subjects.

Q2   Write two headings — Free Press and Censorship.
Write each statement from the box under one of the headings.

It's up to the press
to ensure that what
they publish is true.

The government could
cover up stories that
make them look bad.

The government can't
easily prevent a story
being published.

The press can publish
stories which are
upsetting for the
people involved.

The government
could make sure
there are lots of
stories that make
them look good.

It's up to the press
to ensure that what
they publish is fair.

Newspapers can be
prevented from
printing intrusive or
tasteless articles.

Q3   The UK press isn't censored but they can be prosecuted for revealing some information.

a)   Explain why newspapers wouldn't normally print each of these things.

The name of a child who's on trial for murder.

The name of a police informer.

_An editorial saying why somebody on trial for
fraud shouldn't be convicted._

b)   Explain what a 'gagging order' is.

Q4   Imagine you live in a Communist country where the government censors the news.

Get hold of a copy of today's newspaper. In a group go through the paper crossing
out everything that you think the government might like to censor.

How much have you crossed out? Explain why you censored each item.

Regulating the Media

Q1   These questions are about the way newspapers are regulated.

   a)   In the UK newspapers are 'self-regulated'. What does this mean?

   b)   The organisation which manages the voluntary code of practice for the media is called the PCC — what does PCC stand for?

   c)   There are two main areas that people complain to the PCC about. Choose which ones they are from the box.

invasion of privacy		late payment of fees	trespassing
	poor quality photos		biased reporting

   d)   What happens if the Committee agrees that the complaint is justified?

Q2   There are lots of different organisations that deal with complaints about the media.

   a)   Who would you contact if you wanted to complain about a really racy episode of "The Archers" that upset your gran?

   b)   Who would you contact if you wanted to complain about a TV advertisement that was making your little brother completely obsessed with a bright orange sugary drink?

   c)   Who would you contact if you wanted to complain about a TV documentary claiming that you are Lord Lucan?

Q3   Write a mini-essay explaining why the internet is so much harder to regulate than other media.

> Think about the huge numbers of websites on the internet and the fact it's fairly new.

DISCUSSION QUESTION Q4   Read these statements about journalism.

> If journalists never printed information that might be just the slightest bit untrue, the news would be so boring.

> A journalist should never print or broadcast a story unless they're 100% sure that everything in it is true.

> It's alright to exaggerate in stories about celebrities — they should realise that's the kind of thing that happens when you're famous.

Explain whether you agree or disagree with each of these statements.

DISCUSSION QUESTION Q5   What problems could there be if advertising wasn't regulated? Think about the claims advertisers make and how much we are influenced by advertising.

Thank you OFCOM for making my TV safe — sigh...

Media regulation's a tricky balance. On the one hand freedom of expression's really important but on the other hand no one wants TV, radio and newspapers spouting any old nonsense. Oh no no.

Media Laws

Q1   Explain why a newspaper or news programme could be prosecuted for each of the following.

a) Broadcasting a story saying a bishop had been caught shoplifting whisky which turned out not to be true.

b) Printing a story saying a government minister had an embarrassing medical condition.

c) Printing a photograph of a naked popstar in a magazine aimed at girls in their early teens.

d) Broadcasting an interview with a British spy and giving away his name.

e) Revealing the Army's plans for a major battle the night before it happens.

f) Publishing information connected with a murder case before the case has gone to court.

Q2   Match each law with what it says.

a) Official Secrets Act

b) Obscene Publications Act

c) Defamation Law

If a newspaper tells a story about someone that isn't true, this is known as libel, and the person can sue for damages.	It's a criminal offence for newspapers to print anything that a court judges to be obscene.	Anything that's classed as an official secret, e.g. information about national defence, can't be printed or broadcast.

Q3   Which of these would be likely punishments for a newspaper that's been found guilty of libel?

> _Editor goes to prison._
>
> _Newspaper has to print a public apology explaining they got the facts wrong._
>
> _Newspaper has to pay compensation to the person they libelled._
>
> _Newspaper is closed down._
>
> _Journalist who wrote the article not allowed to work in the media any more._

 Q4   Read about this real-life case involving the media, then answer the questions below.

> In 2003 Catherine Zeta-Jones and Michael Douglas were awarded compensation of £500,000 after 'Hello' magazine published photos of their wedding without their permission. They claimed the magazine had invaded their privacy even though they had already had photos of their wedding published in another magazine.

Do you think they deserved to get this much money?

Changing Things Through the Media

Q1   Newspapers, radio and TV are all useful sources of information.

Write down as many types of information as you can think of, which we get from the media. Include information from things like documentaries as well as current affairs.

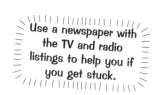
Use a newspaper with the TV and radio listings to help you if you get stuck.

Q2   The basic news articles in a newspaper are supposed to be unbiased, but other articles openly present opinions. Say what kind of opinion each of these types of article presents.

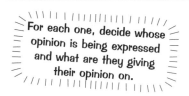
For each one, decide whose opinion is being expressed and what are they giving their opinion on.

a)   editorial

b)   letters page

c)   album review

d)   celebrity gossip column

e)   political comment by e.g. an MP

f)   TV review

Q3   For each programme or type of article in the box below suggest how it could change the way people think or act.

> home makeover show
>
> radio station playing current music
>
> TV documentary about a politician spending a week living in the "real world" on benefits
>
> TV celebrity talking about their favourite books
>
> documentary about a famine in Africa
>
> newspaper campaign to legalise cannabis

DISCUSSION QUESTION Q4   Some newspapers in the UK are traditionally seen as being more 'right wing' and others are seen as being more 'left wing'.

- Talk about newspapers you, your family and friends read.

- What biases do you think the different newspapers have?

- Do you think you are influenced by the opinions presented in the newspapers?

e.g. The Guardian is seen as a left wing paper and The Telegraph is seen as more right wing.

DISCUSSION QUESTION Q5   For this one you need a copy of a newspaper.

Choose five articles with photos. Read each article and look at the photos carefully. Talk about what the article is saying and what the photo is saying. Do they say the same thing?

A photo of a suspected murderer could make him look really scary even though the article makes it clear he's only under suspicion not actually guilty.

And now a message from our sponsors...

CGP SPLAM*, a delicious new tinned pork luncheon meat product, is a tasty snack any time of day. Tests show it can boost brain activity and help you to lose height (only as part of a balanced diet).

*Special offer: Free 750g tin of CGP SPLAM with every 10 CGP books you buy. Offer ends last week.

Who Owns the Media?

Q1 Country A has a state-owned and controlled media. Country B has privately-owned media.
For each of the descriptions below say whether it's more likely to apply to Country A or B.

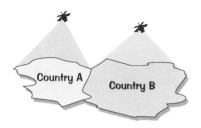

a) Media usually supports government policies.

b) In the run up to an election different papers
and programmes support different parties.

c) In the run up to an election all media supports the ruling party.

d) Media is often critical of government policies.

e) Stories which could embarrass the government, e.g. about a
minister who's been taking backhanders from an arms dealer
don't usually get reported.

Q2 Say whether each of these would be an example of commercial or political bias.

a) A copy of a newspaper which mentions all the reasons the Conservatives oppose a
government policy, but none of the Liberal Democrats' reasons.

b) A film review programme which only reviews films made by one Hollywood studio.

c) A newspaper which puts an environmental issue on the front page every other day.

d) A newspaper which runs stories on problems caused by asylum seekers every other day.

e) A radio station which plays music from one record company far more
often than music from other record companies.

DISCUSSION QUESTION Q3 Read these statements.

"Before you read a tabloid
newspaper you have to take your
brain out and put it in a drawer."

"I don't call Jordan's cup size
important national news."

Do you think it's right for tabloid newspapers to 'give the punters what they want' or
should all newspapers include as much serious news as sport and celebrity gossip?

DISCUSSION QUESTION Q4 From the mid-1990s The Sun began supporting New Labour. Many people think
this support was a big factor in Tony Blair's government getting elected in 1997.

Do you think it is fair that newspaper owners can have a big influence on political
opinion? Do you think that the radio and TV news also try to influence public opinion?

Exclusive: Justin shows nostril hair at concert (see the pics on p46)

You might say that page after page of stories about Aguilera's zits and partial sightings of Justin's
Y-fronts is just mindless trash, but everyone seems to want to read it. And as long as it sells,
newspapers are going to print it. So show us Peter's pants and let's see some celebs with cellulite...

At School

Q1   A school is a kind of community.

    a)   List all the different groups of people who take part in the life of your school.

    b)   What makes a school a community rather than a random collection of people?

Q2   "The key to a satisfying school career is participation."
Quote from *My Years at the Chalk Face* by Mr. Squeers.

    a)   Write a definition of 'participation'.

    b)   What kind of activities can you participate in at your school
(apart from turning up to lessons and picking your nose in assembly)?

Q3   "The single biggest factor in making the atmosphere in a school good or bad is the way people behave."

Don't just put stuff that students do — have a moan about your teachers too if you need to.

    a)   Make a list of things that make life at your school less pleasant for everyone there, and another listing the positive things about your school.

    b)   For each of your negative points in a) suggest a way of improving or dealing with the problem.

DISCUSSION QUESTION   Q4   Read these statements.

By the age of 16 I'll have spent about 15,000 hours of my life at school. I might as well join in with things now and then.

School is dreadful. I'm just killing time until I can get out of here, get a job and get a life.

All I expect to get out of school is some GCSE results.

Which of these statements do you agree with most?
What do you think is the best way to make use of your time at school?
What can you learn apart from the stuff that gets tested in exams?

School days — the happiest days of your life...

If you just don't see yourself being one of those joining-in types try motivating yourself with some selfish reasons — it's good for your CV and it's all free. And just maybe it'll turn out to be fun...

In the Community

Q1   A community is any group of people living in the same area or working together.

   a)   Write down as many different types of community as you can think of.

   b)   What communities are you a part of?

Q2   Explain how each of these activities could benefit a community.

   a)   Travelling by bike instead of by car.

   b)   Charity fundraising.

   c)   Litter picking at school.

   d)   Collecting groceries for your neighbour.

   e)   Joining a local Friends of the Earth group.

   f)   Teaching canoeing to young people at a local canoe club.

   g)   Planting trees in a community garden.

Q3   Make a list of community activities you could get involved in in your area.

Your local library will have shelves groaning with information on this kind of thing.

Q4   In the UK, we throw away about 165 million tonnes of 'waste' every year — that's the same weight as approximately 40 million buses.

   Explain how a local recycling project could benefit the local community and the global community.

 Q5   'Why should I waste my time doing community work? It won't make a difference anyway.'

   What do you think?

It's better than the other kind of community service...

No one's suggesting you go out and do something you really hate for some kind of theoretical brownie points. But if there is something you're into you might as well do it with other people.

51

Have Your Say

Q1 Some people's arguments tend to be based on opinions. Others rely more on facts.

a) Explain the difference between an opinion and a fact.

b) Explain why opinions are more convincing when they are based on facts.

Q2 The local council is planning to sell your school sports field to housing developers. There is going to be a public meeting at your school to discuss the sale.

a) Decide whether you would be for or against the sale if this really happened. Write down your opinion.

b) Write down what facts you would need to know to get your opinion across effectively.

c) Write down where you would find the facts you need to back up your opinion.

Q3 For each issue below choose from the box at least one way to get your opinion about it heard.

> The government has announced that they are thinking about banning mobile phones for under-18s.

> The governors of your school have decided that your uniform should be purple with yellow spots.

> The council is encouraging a chemical company to set up a factory near a local nature reserve.

| Write to the local paper. | Write an article for your school magazine. | Write to a national paper. | Write to your MP. | Use flyers and posters. |

DISCUSSION QUESTION Q4 "If you feel strongly about an issue tell everyone about it over and over again. They'll get the message in the end."

Is this true? How effective would this approach be?

DISCUSSION QUESTION Q5 A friend of yours is going to speak in public but he's really, really nervous.

What advice can you give him to make sure his speech goes smoothly.

I say, I say, I say...

I've got a friend who is very, very good at ranting about things that bother him. He's passionate, articulate and stabs his finger into the table to back up his points. He doesn't always listen though.

Organising Stuff

Q1 Teams work better when everyone has a clear role.

a) Explain what a 'role' is.

b) Why does a team work better when everyone has a clear role?
    Give as many reasons as you can.

Q2 You're organising a sponsored bed push to raise money for Comic Relief.

a) Work out everything that needs doing to make it happen and split it up into separate tasks.
b) Decide how many people you need to help you.

Q3 Put these tasks into an order that would help a project run smoothly.

> There's no perfect way of doing this so there's more than one 'right' answer.

SET DEADLINES FOR TASKS
EVALUATE THE PROJECT
AGREE AIMS OF THE PROJECT
BREAK PLAN INTO SEPARATE TASKS
ALLOCATE ROLES
RUN THE PROJECT
DECIDE ON CONTINGENCY PLANS
AGREE AN ACTION PLAN

Q4 Write down which of these would help a team run smoothly.

clear communication   including members in decision making   cups of tea   members taking personal responsibility
encouraging others   taking notes   having a clear plan

 Q5 How can you tell whether a project's been successful or not?

> Do you just get a feel for it, or can you measure it in some way?

 Q6 "The more people involved in a project, the better the project will be."

Do you agree with this statement?

What do you call a hideous beast with many heads...

A team where everyone thinks they're in charge... It's important that everyone has a worthwhile role, but things run smoother if one person runs meetings and keeps track of what needs doing.

Using the Community

Q1   You're planning a 'Sports Extravaganza Day' to raise funds for the local hospice. Make a list of organisations you could contact for help and support.

Q2   Explain why each of these would be a good or bad place to promote your event.

local newspaper	local schools
Yellow Pages	cornershop
hospital radio	beauty salon
Job centre	national newspaper

Q3   Suggest how each of these groups could help with your event.

a)   Local businesses

b)   Rotary Clubs

c)   Parent-teacher Association

d)   Friends and neighbours

Q4   Draft a letter to your local Rotary Club asking them to support your event by paying for printing costs for publicity material.

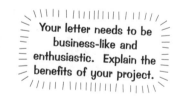
Your letter needs to be business-like and enthusiastic. Explain the benefits of your project.

DISCUSSION QUESTION **Q5**   Everyone who helps with or takes part in an event wants to know if it's been a success. Businesses and individuals who've contributed money will also want to know what happened to their money.

What can the organising group do to inform everyone about the outcome of the event?

Give me a C, give me an O, give — you get the picture...

When you're raising money for a local cause it's easier than you might think to get people to help — it's really obvious where the money's going and donors could benefit themselves one day.

Section Nine — Active Citizenship